Develop Non-Verbal Reasoning

CU00751246

Frequently Asked Questions For Adults

What is this book about?

Develop Non-verbal Reasoning is in level two of the *Practise & Pass 11+* series. It's a workbook for students who are going to take an 11+ test or school entrance exam that includes a non-verbal reasoning section. In it I help students further their knowledge of five key question types they've already worked on in level one of the series, and introduce one new question type that they'll typically face in the exam. I also provide 180 further original questions to practise.

I provide coaching for students throughout the text. I talk them through the whole process from answering questions to helping them understand their mistakes, so that they have a firm understanding of the basics.

(Note: if they haven't already, I highly recommend that your student work through level one of the series – Discover Non-verbal Reasoning – before starting this book.)

What is non-verbal reasoning?

Non-verbal reasoning is the solving of problems that involve shapes and patterns. Typically non-verbal questions involve looking for similarities or differences between shapes or patterns. This kind of question is not generally taught in schools.

How do I use this book?

This book is divided into bite-sized lessons for the student to work through. Each lesson covers a specific type of question and is set up in the same way:

1 I explain the question type, giving the student an understanding of what they need to know.

2 I provide one or two worked examples to show how the question type is best tackled.

(Note: I do recommend that an adult reads through the explanation and example(s) with the student to ensure they have a firm understanding of what is required.)

3 When ready, the student should work through the first set of practice questions on their own and mark their answers on the answer sheet provided.

Important: unlike in level one an adult should mark this set of questions, and all the questions in this book. The answers can be found on pages 103 and 104. You might want to cut these out of the book so the temptation for the student to take a peek is removed!

4 I provide a summary of what the student's score means and give hints on how to improve it, if needs be, and on how they can speed up their work.

(Note: the student should discuss any errors and talk through the hints together with an adult so that any problems are dealt with straight away.)

5 Next, there is a second set of practice questions but this time there are 20 questions for the student to work through so that they get used to concentrating for a longer time period. The student shouldn't work on these until they understand why they made mistakes first-time around.

6 Finally there is a score sheet on page 100 which should be completed after each lesson to keep a record of progress. This can be used to identify those question types the student needs to practise more.

(Note: occasionally I will include a question that hasn't been explained in the lesson. This is by design: the student will very likely come up against a question they are not familiar with in the actual test so it's important that they get used to applying the knowledge they have to work out the right answer.)

Why does this book feature multiple choice answers?

Multiple choice answers are becoming the most common format for the 11+. This means that five possible answers are given for each question and they are presented to the student in a grid format. To answer the question correctly the student has to put a horizontal line in the empty box next to the correct answer.

⇨ It's important that students learn to use these answer grids correctly from the outset so they can avoid making common errors, such as marking the wrong box or accidentally missing out questions.

⇨ Make sure you find out from the examination centre whether the multiple choice format will be used in the final exam so you're confident that the student is doing the right preparation.

When should the student start to prepare for the exam and how often should they practise?

The sooner the student starts to prepare for the exam the better. Realistically, I suggest there should be a full year's run-up to the test so that the student has a chance to practise as many of the subject areas and question types that might appear in the exam as possible without having to study for hours and hours each week. This means working through all three levels of the *Practise & Pass 11+* series (this book is in level two of the series) at a steady and realistic pace.

For this book I recommend students work at the pace of one lesson a week which means six weeks in total. However, if a student, is able there is nothing to stop them moving through the book at a quicker pace.

What's the best way for a student to study?

⇨ It's important that the student gets used to a test-type environment so they should have a clear space to work in, with no distractions. This means the TV and all music should be switched off, the student should be sat at a table and there should be a clock in clear view so that they can time themselves.

⇨ Students should use a pencil to answer the questions and have an eraser and some scrap paper to hand which they can use for any workings out.

(Note: I highly recommend that the student avoids practising on the same days that they have school homework and that they also have other extra-curricular activities – this means they have other outlets for their energies and don't become overworked or stressed, or too bored with the practice.)

How quickly should a student answer the questions?

As this book is in level two of the series, students should be used to the question types so I do expect them to get up to speed. They should follow the timings I have provided so that they work at a 'real time' pace. I have provided 'tips for speeding up' throughout the book to help with this. Typically in the actual exam they will have 30 minutes to answer 60 questions (although, do check this with the examination centre as timings can vary).

What score should the student be aiming for?

Remember that 11+ tests and entrance examinations are tough to pass. I have written this book to reflect that fact, so it is unlikely that the student will sail through the book scoring 100% in each lesson.

After the first set of practice questions in every lesson, I have given a target score for that particular question type – this is based on my experience of teaching them year on year and should help you assess how the student is doing, and what areas, if any, need work. I also include helpful tips on how students can improve, and recommend they use the 'vocabulary builder'.

I should add that the scores here in no way indicate whether the student will definitely pass or fail the exam; they are only here as a guide.

What is the 'vocabulary builder'?

The vocabulary builder exercise is an extra task to help improve the student's vocabulary.

What should I do once this book is completed?

I recommend that the student move on to level three of the series: *Practice Tests*. This provides full practice test papers for your child to work through so that they know exactly what to expect on test day.

LESSON 1 Solving Analogical Shapes

In this exercise, you're given a pair of analogical shapes, that is, two shapes which are related in some way. You're then given a third shape and have to work out which of the answer choices is related to the third shape in the same way as the first two shapes are related to each other.

Let's look at an example to remind you how to do this.

Example

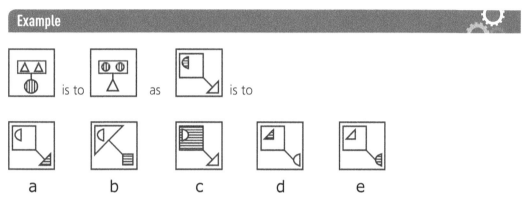

a　　　　　b　　　　　c　　　　　d　　　　　e

Here's how to solve this question:

⇨ Start by looking at the first two shapes. Note that in the second one, the shapes inside the rectangle have swapped places with the shape at the bottom. Looking at the third diagram you can see that the answer should have a semi-circle at the bottom and a triangle inside the square. This rules out answer choices a, b and c so you can cross them out.

⇨ You should now notice that although the shapes change places they keep their shading. So you need a shape that has a semi-circle with stripes at the bottom. This means that your answer must be e.

LESSON 1 PART 1

Now look at the questions below. Try to do each one as quickly as you can, but make sure you finish them all. When you've found the answer, mark it on the answer sheet on page 9. When you've finished, write down the time you took in the box above. Remember to get an adult to mark the test for you, then write down your score in the box at the top of this page.

You have five minutes to complete these, so work quickly.

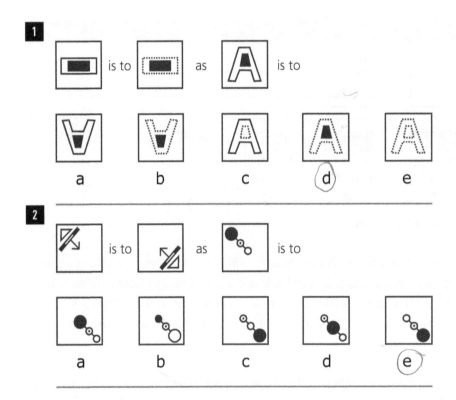

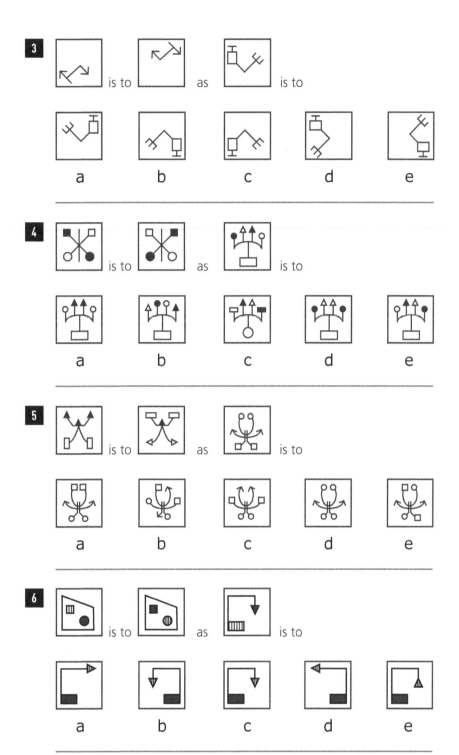

3

is to [ ] as [ ] is to

a   b   c   d   e

4

is to [ ] as [ ] is to

a   b   c   d   e

5

is to [ ] as [ ] is to

a   b   c   d   e

6

is to [ ] as [ ] is to

a   b   c   d   e

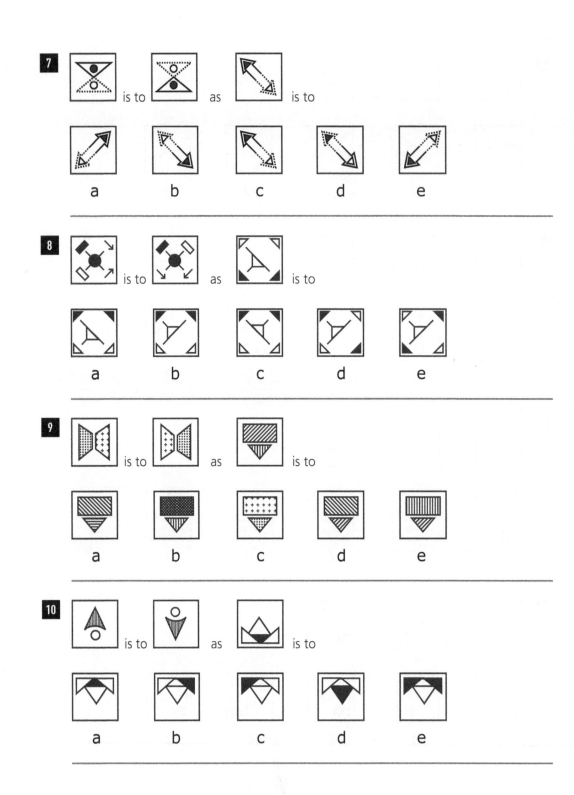

LESSON 1 PART 1: ANSWER SHEET

Mark your answer by putting a horizontal line in one of the boxes as in the example below.

Example:

 # How Did You Do?
Let's Find Out!

Remember, there is no self-marking in this book. Please ask an adult to mark your answers.

If you scored 8 or more out of 10

That's a great score. Check the ones you got wrong and make sure you understand why. Then read the tips for speeding up before you try the next set of questions.

If you scored fewer than 8 out of 10

You'll need to improve this score so check to see where you went wrong. Did you complete all the questions in the time? It's not a very long test, so make sure you work quickly. Read the tips for speeding up before moving on.

TIPS FOR SPEEDING UP

- If you find a question tricky, move on and come back to it – don't let it stop you from doing the others.

- Remember to cross off the wrong choices to help you find the correct one. This is the easiest way to get these questions right.

- Remember to track one property at a time and try to choose one that's easy to see – this will help you eliminate some wrong answers quickly.

LESSON 1 PART 2

My Time

My Score

The big practice

This part has 20 questions instead of the usual 10. Examinations often give you non-verbal reasoning questions in banks of 20, so treat this as a realistic practice. The aim is to help you get used to answering this many questions before you move on to *Practise & Pass 11 + Level Three: Practice Test Papers*.

Try to do each question as quickly as you can, but make sure you finish them all. When you've found the answer, mark it on the corresponding answer sheet on page 19. When you've finished, write down the time you took in the box above, and again get an adult to mark the test for you. Then write down your score in the box at the top of this page.

You have 10 minutes to complete these 20 questions, which are of mixed difficulty. This is your final practice on this type of question, so try to do your best.

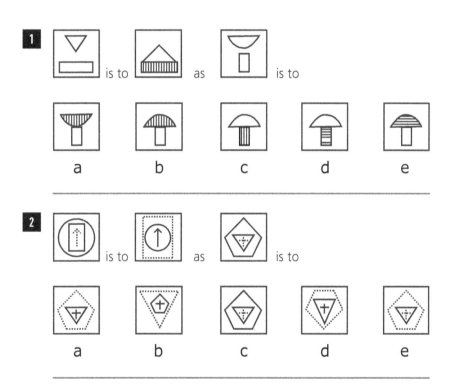

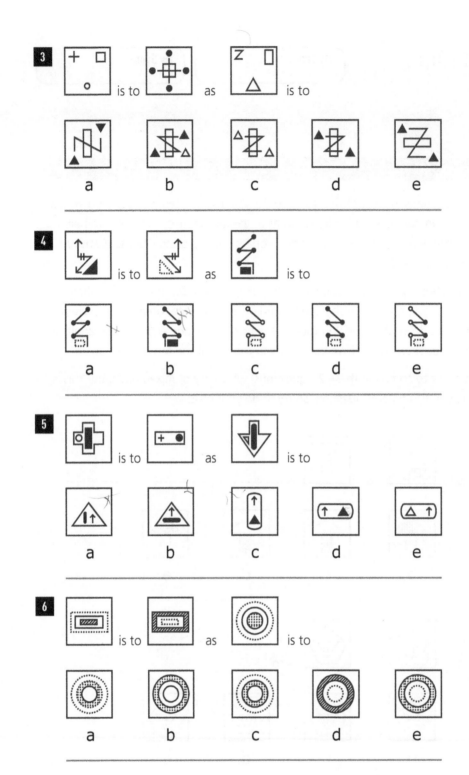

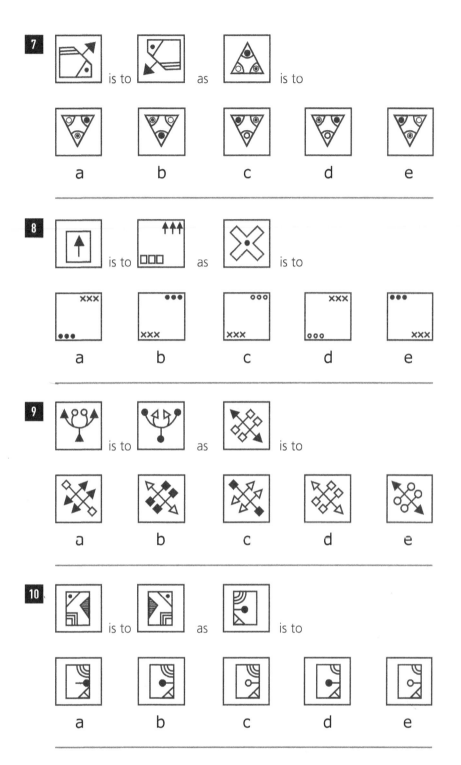

7 is to ... as ... is to

a b c d e

8 is to ... as ... is to

a b c d e

9 is to ... as ... is to

a b c d e

10 is to ... as ... is to

a b c d e

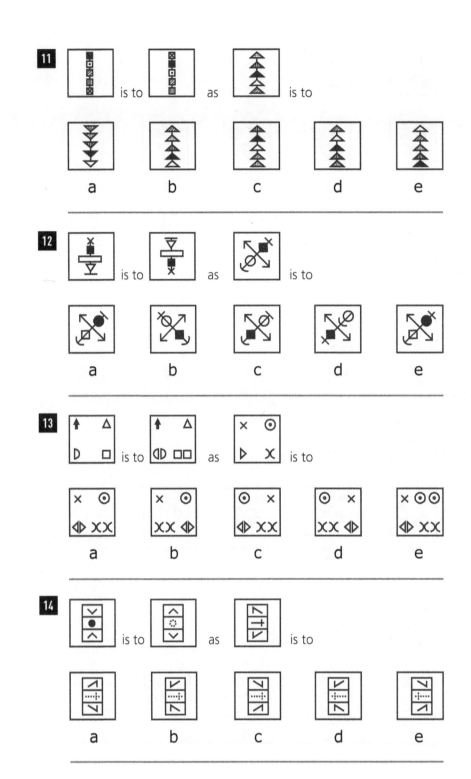

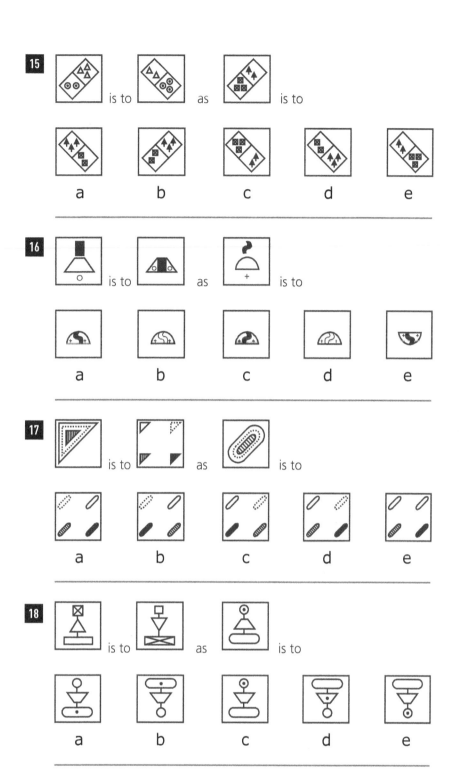

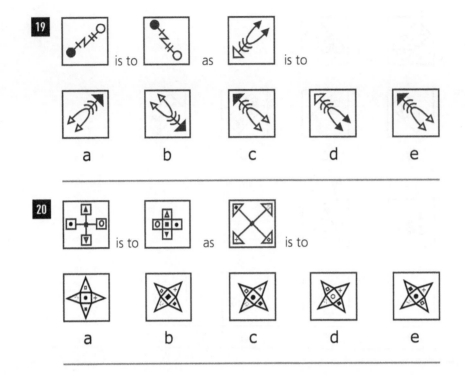

LESSON 1 PART 2: ANSWER SHEET

Mark your answer by putting a horizontal line in one of the boxes as in the example below.

Example:

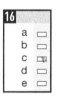

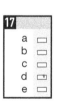

LESSON 2 Finding the Shape that Belongs to a Group

In this exercise, you'll look first at the group of shapes in the oval. Then you'll need to decide which of the five possible answers would best fit into the group. Let's take a look at an example to remind you how to do this.

Example

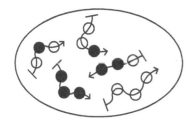

a   b   c   d   e

⇨ Start by looking at the group of shapes in the oval. You can see that all the shapes are arrows with circles placed on them. Some of the circles are shaded and some aren't, so the arrows don't all have that in common.

⇨ Now count the circles – each arrow has three. So you should be looking for an arrow with three circles, regardless of shading.

⇨ Now look at the choices a–e, you can see that only one has three circles on an arrow – choice <u>b</u>. This is the answer you should mark on your answer grid.

LESSON 2 PART 1

My Time

My Score

Now look at the questions below. Try to do each one as quickly as you can but make sure you finish them all. When you've found the answer, mark it on the corresponding answer sheet on page 25. When you've finished, write down the time you took in the box above. Remember to get an adult to mark the test for you. Then write your score in the box at the top of this page.

You have five minutes to complete this task, so work quickly.

1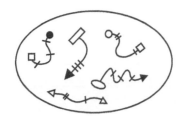

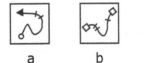

a   b   c   d   e

2

a   b   c   d   e

3

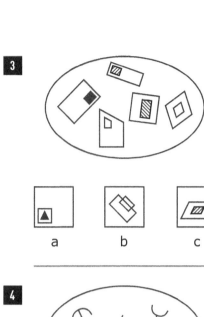

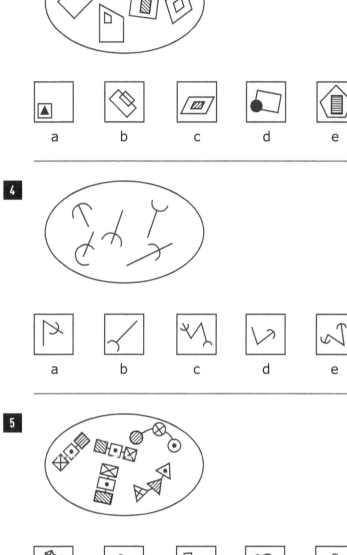

a   b   c   d   e

4

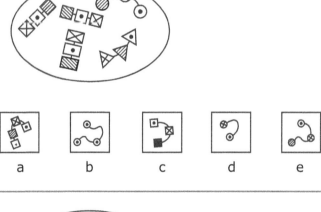

a   b   c   d   e

5

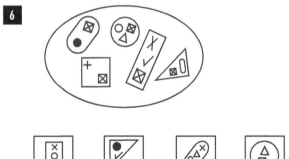

a   b   c   d   e

6

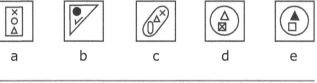

a   b   c   d   e

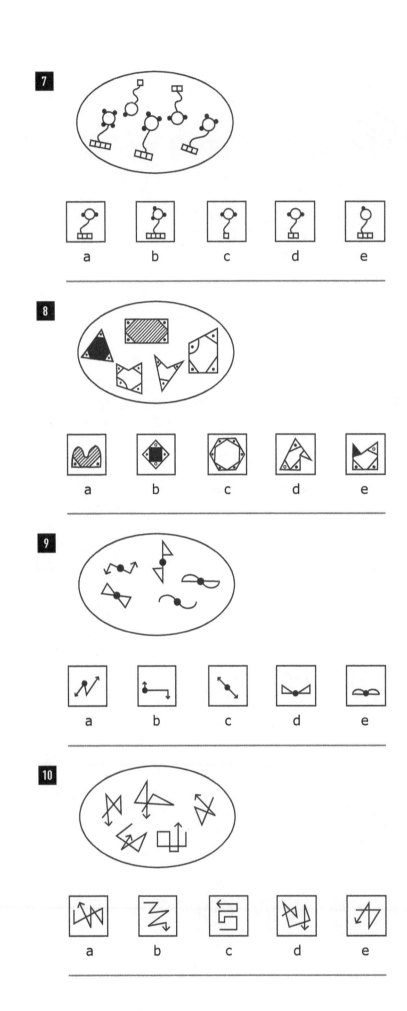

LESSON 2 PART 1: ANSWER SHEET

Mark your answer by putting a horizontal line in one of the boxes as in the example below.

Example:

 # How Did You Do? Let's Find Out!

If you scored 8 or more out of 10

Great stuff! You're doing well because these questions can be tough. Read the tips for speeding up then move on to the next set of questions.

If you scored fewer than 8 out of 10

These are tough questions but you need to keep working hard to improve this score. Read the tips for speeding up and try the next set of questions.

TIPS FOR SPEEDING UP

- Remember to cross off the wrong answers to help you find the correct one. This is the easiest way to get these right.

- You only have 30 seconds for each question, so you must really work quickly on these! Don't spend too long on a question that's tricky – you can always come back to it at the end.

- Try keeping one finger of one hand on the question you are looking at and one finger of the other hand on the same question number on the answer sheet – this will save you time and help to stop you making any errors when filling in your answer.

- Make sure that every shape has something in common.

- Don't think that you have to spend the same amount of time thinking about each question – sometimes the properties that all the shapes have in common in a question are quite straightforward!

LESSON 2 PART 2

My Time

My Score

The big practice

Here are the questions for your big practice. Try to do each one as quickly as you can but make sure you finish them all. When you've found the answer mark it on the answer sheet on page 35. When you've finished, write down the time you took in the box above. Again, remember to get an adult to mark the test for you, then write your score in the box at the top of this page.

You have 10 minutes to complete these 20 questions, so work quickly. This is your final practice on this type of question, so try to do your best.

1

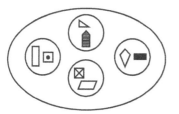

   a   b   c   d   e

2

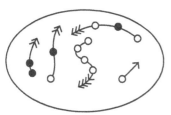

   a   b   c   d   e

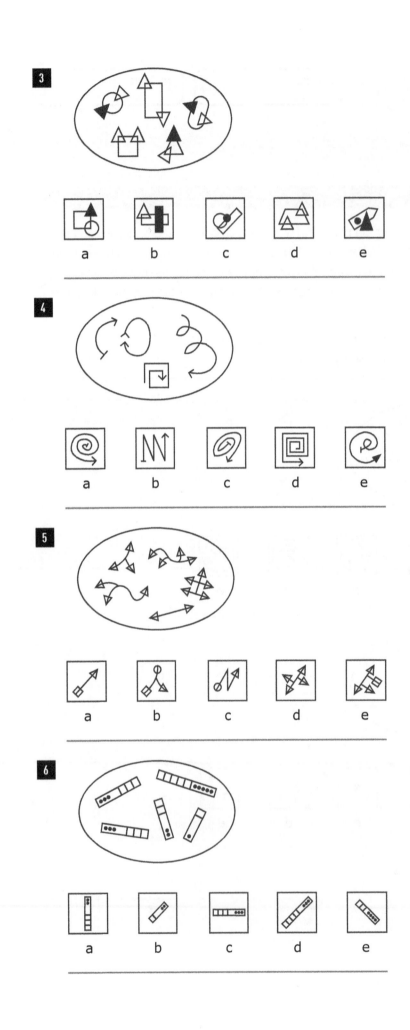

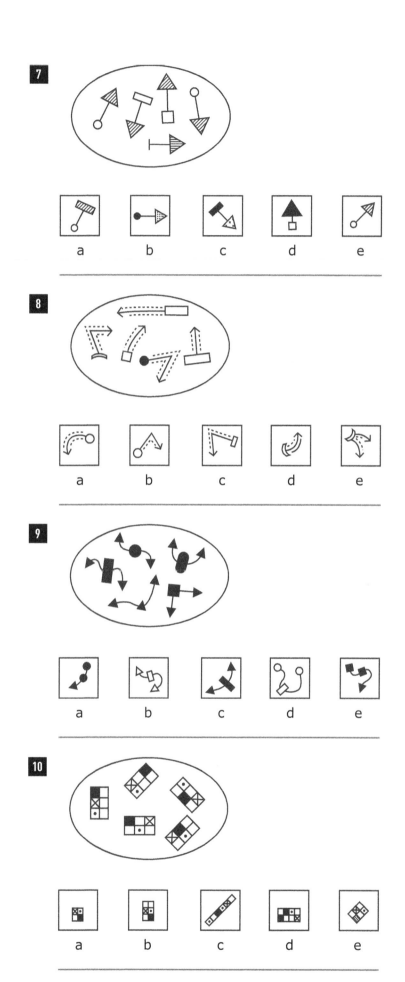

7

a b c d e

8

a b c d e

9

a b c d e

10

a b c d e

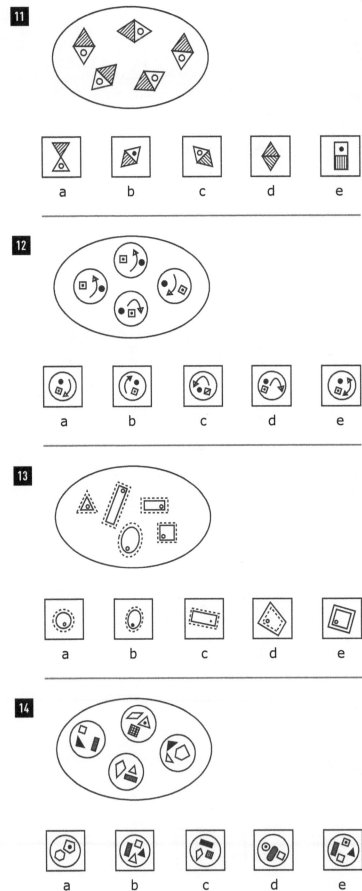

11

a   b   c   d   e

12

a   b   c   d   e

13

a   b   c   d   e

14

a   b   c   d   e

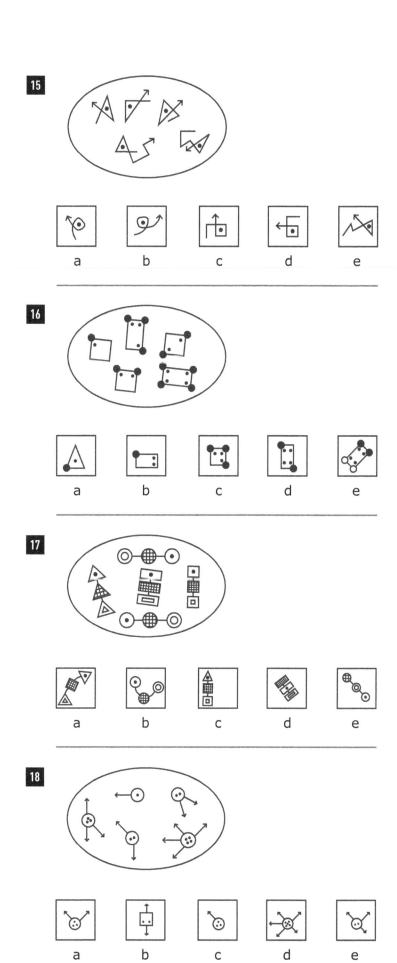

15

a   b   c   d   e

16

a   b   c   d   e

17

a   b   c   d   e

18

a   b   c   d   e

19

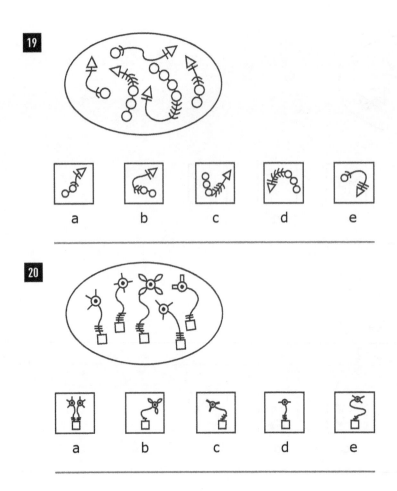

a   b   c   d   e

20

a   b   c   d   e

LESSON 2 PART 2: ANSWER SHEET

Mark your answer by putting a horizontal line in one of the boxes as in the example below.

Example:

LESSON 3 Completing Sequences

In this exercise, you'll need to find the shape or pattern that will best complete the sequence. Let's look at an example to remind you how to do this.

Example

Here's how to solve this question:

⇨ Start by looking at the patterns. It's best to choose an easy property to track first – in this case it's the circle of solid colour. Notice that the position of this circle has changed from the top right segment in the first diagram to the bottom left segment in the second diagram. Following the position of this circle in each diagram, you can conclude that your answer should have the shaded circle back in the place where it was in the very first diagram in the sequence – the top right segment. Answers c and e have it in a different place so you can cross these out.

⇨ Then look at the circle with a cross inside it. You can see that each time it moves round one segment in a clockwise direction. Therefore your answer should have it in the bottom right segment. This means your answer should be <u>d</u>, so that's the letter you should mark on your answer sheet.

LESSON 3 PART 1

Now look at the questions below. For this first set of questions, I've left out the last part of the sequence each time. I've also kept the sequences quite simple – but watch out, they'll get harder in the next part!

Try to do each one as quickly as you can but make sure you finish them all. Mark your answers on the answer sheet on page 41. When you've finished, write down the time you took in the box above. Remember to get an adult to mark the test for you, then write your score in the box at the top of this page.

You have five minutes to complete this task, so work quickly!

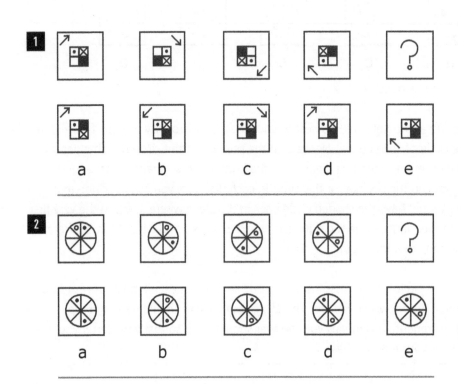

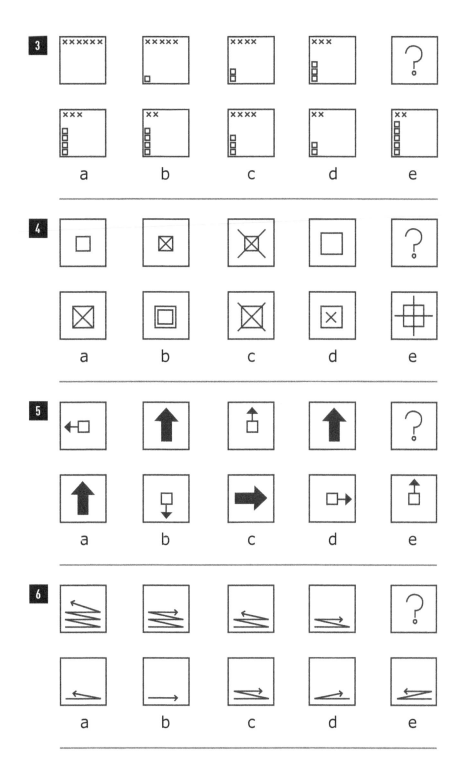

3

a b c d e

4

a b c d e

5

a b c d e

6

a b c d e

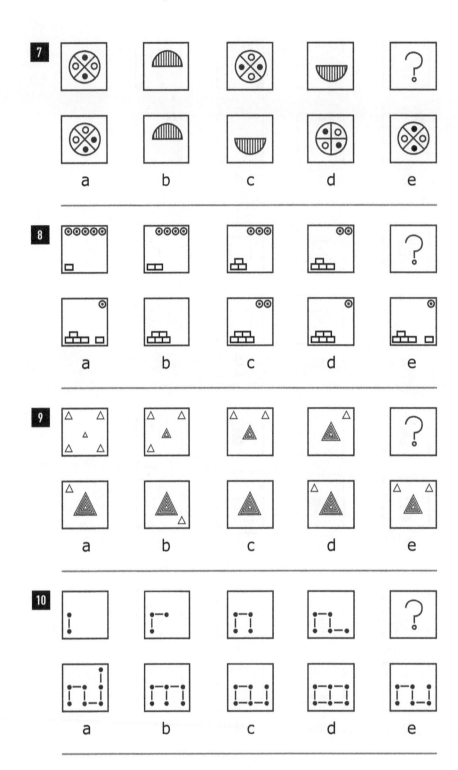

7

a b c d e

8

a b c d e

9

a b c d e

10

a b c d e

LESSON 3 PART 1: ANSWER SHEET

Mark your answer by putting a horizontal line in one of the boxes as in the example below.

Example:

 How Did You Do?
Let's Find Out!

If you scored 8 or more out of 10

This score is a good one, well done! Read the tips for speeding up, and then move on to the next set of questions.

If you scored fewer than 8 out of 10

Check where you went wrong and make sure you understand why so you can avoid these mistakes next time. Read the tips for speeding up before you move on.

TIPS FOR SPEEDING UP

- Look for easy properties to track first – these will help you eliminate answers which are obviously wrong. Remember to cross them out.

- Look for detailed properties when you are down to the last two or three choices.

- If the first part of the sequence is missing, work from right to left – this will make it easier and quicker to spot the sequence.

LESSON 3 PART 2

My Time

My Score

The big practice

Here are the questions for your big practice. Try to do each one as quickly as you can, but make sure you finish them all. When you've found the answer, mark it on the answer sheet on page 51. When you've finished, write down the time you took in the box above. Again, get an adult to mark the test for you, then write your score in the box at the top of this page.

You have 10 minutes to complete these 20 questions, so work quickly. This is your final practice on this type of question, so do try your best.

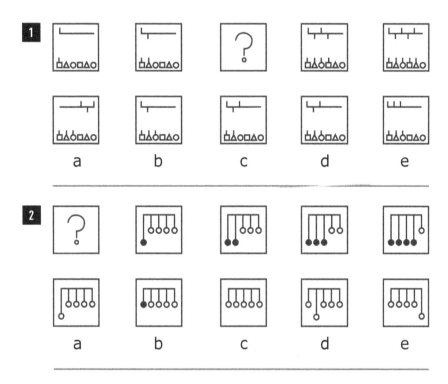

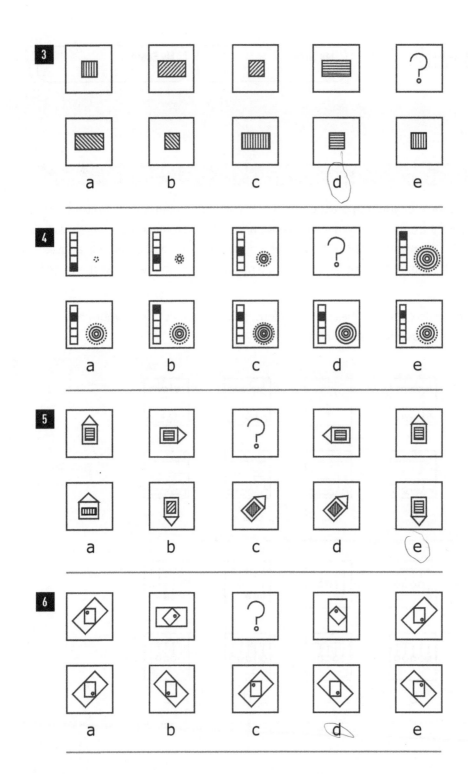

3

a   b   c   d   e

4

a   b   c   d   e

5

a   b   c   d   e

6

a   b   c   d   e

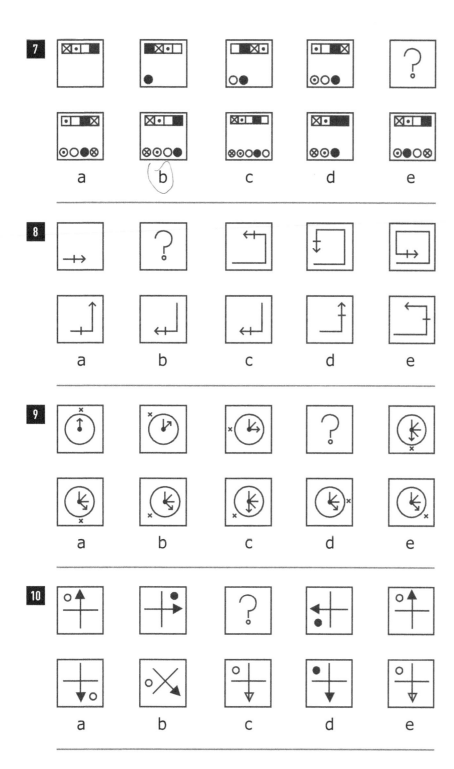

7

a   b   c   d   e

8

a   b   c   d   e

9

a   b   c   d   e

10

a   b   c   d   e

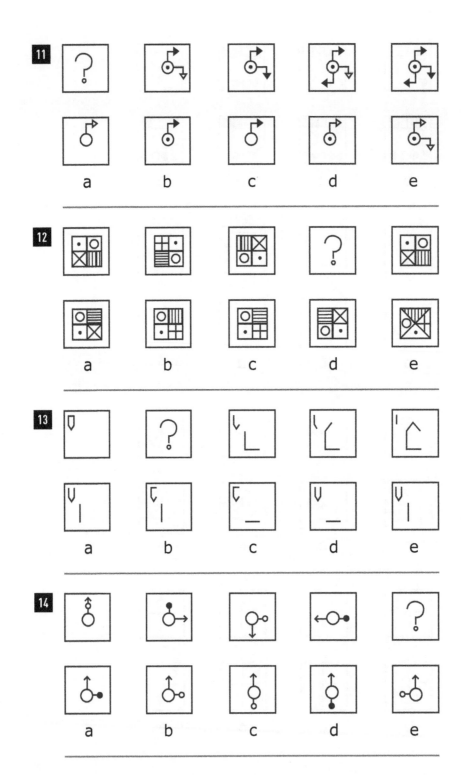

11

a   b   c   d   e

12

a   b   c   d   e

13

a   b   c   d   e

14

a   b   c   d   e

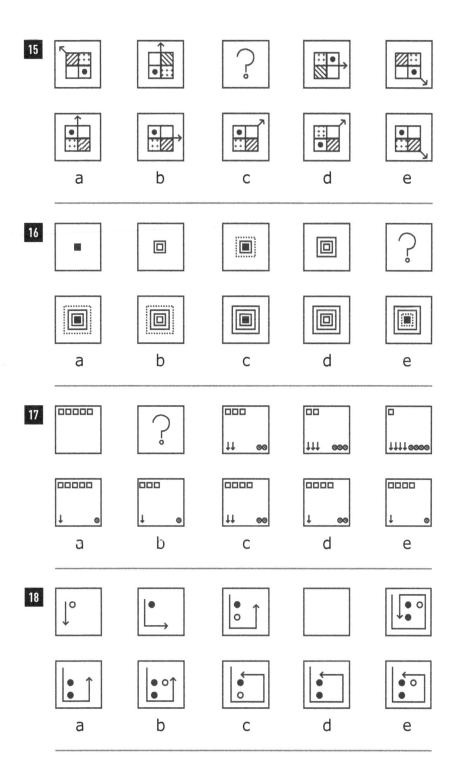

15

a   b   c   d   e

16

a   b   c   d   e

17

a   b   c   d   e

18

a   b   c   d   e

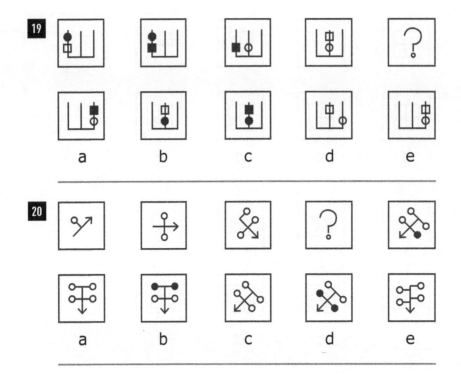

LESSON 3 PART 2: ANSWER SHEET

Mark your answer by putting a horizontal line in one of the boxes as in the example below.

Example:

  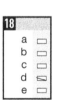

LESSON 4 Working Out Codes

In this exercise, you're given two or more shapes along with letter codes that represent these shapes. You're then given another shape and you have to work out what letter code represents this shape.

To answer these questions correctly you must first work out which letters represent which properties. To do this, look at the shapes you've been given and try to find a property that they each share. When you find it look at the letters and you'll find that shapes with the same property have the same letter. This will tell you which letter represents which property.

Let's look at an example to remind you how it works.

Example

A CH
B DG
C DC
D CD
E HG

Here's how to solve this question:

⇨ Start by looking for similarities between the three shapes with codes. You can see that there are two circles with horizontal stripes in their left-hand segment and they both have the bottom letter H. The shape with vertical lines has the bottom letter G and the last circle also has vertical lines so it should have G as its bottom letter. Only choices b and e have this letter so you can cross out the rest.

⇨ Next look at the small circles in the right-hand segment. The two shapes with a cross in the circles have the top letter C and the shape with the circle of solid colour has the top letter D. So the missing code should be DG, and so you would mark letter b as your final answer.

LESSON 4 PART 1

My Time

My Score

Now look at the questions below. Try to do each one as quickly as you can, but make sure you finish them all. When you've found the answer, mark it on the answer sheet on page 57. When you've finished, write down the time you took in the box above. Remember to get an adult to mark the test for you, then write down your score in the box at the top of this page.

You have five minutes to complete this test, so work quickly.

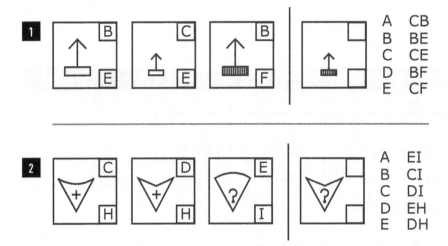

1

A CB
B BE
C CE
D BF
E CF

2

A EI
B CI
C DI
D EH
E DH

3

A ME
B LE
C MF
D MD
E LD

4

A CH
B DG
C DC
D CD
E HG

5

A UG
B TF
C UE
D TE
E UF

6

A VC
B VB
C WC
D WB
E VW

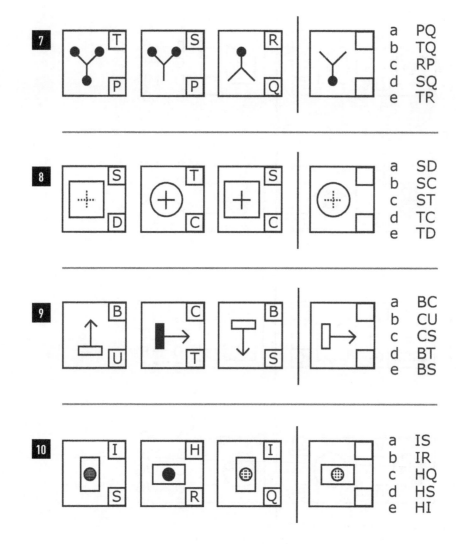

7

a PQ
b TQ
c RP
d SQ
e TR

8

a SD
b SC
c ST
d TC
e TD

9

a BC
b CU
c CS
d BT
e BS

10

a IS
b IR
c HQ
d HS
e HI

LESSON 4 PART 1: ANSWER SHEET

Mark your answer by putting a horizontal line in one of the boxes as in the example below.

Example:

How Did You Do? Let's Find Out!

If you scored 8 or more out of 10

These questions can be quite difficult, so this is a good score – well done! Read the tips for speeding up then move on to the next set of questions.

If you scored fewer than 8 out of 10

I consider these questions quite difficult – especially when you only have 30 seconds for each one. But you still need to try to improve your score. Look at where you went wrong and try to learn from your mistakes. Read the tips for speeding up before you move on.

TIPS FOR SPEEDING UP

- Don't spend too long on a question that's tricky – you can always come back to it at the end.

- Look for obvious similarities in the shapes and use this to work out the appropriate letter code for that property.

- Once you have worked out the first part of your code, look to the shape for which you need to work out the code. After finding the first correct letter cross out the answer choices that don't have that letter. This will help you narrow your search down and find the correct answer more quickly.

LESSON 4 PART 2

My Time

My Score

The big practice

Here are the questions for your big practice. Try to do each one as quickly as you can, and make sure you finish them all. When you've found the answer mark it on the answer sheet on page 67. When you've finished, write down the time you took in the box above. Again, get an adult to mark the test for you, then write your score in the box at the top of this page.

You have 10 minutes to complete these 20 questions, so work quickly. This is your final practice on this type of question, so try to do your best.

A JC
B HD
C IC
D JD
E HC

A TC
B SC
C RC
D UB
E TB

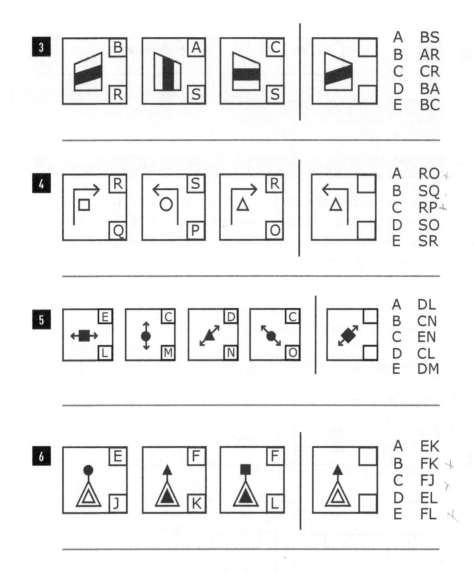

3
A BS
B AR
C CR
D BA
E BC

4
A RO
B SQ
C RP
D SO
E SR

5
A DL
B CN
C EN
D CL
E DM

6
A EK
B FK
C FJ
D EL
E FL

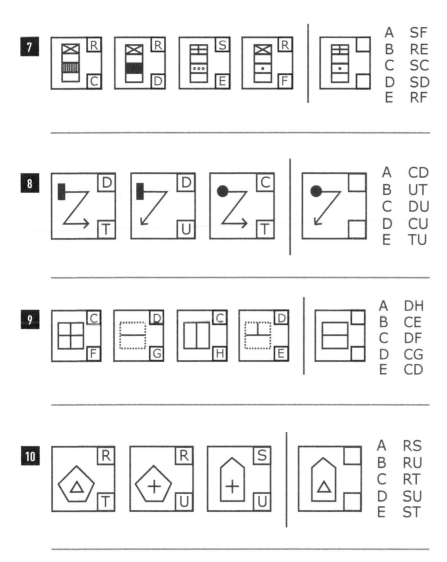

7

A   SF
B   RE
C   SC
D   SD
E   RF

8

A   CD
B   UT
C   DU
D   CU
E   TU

9

A   DH
B   CE
C   DF
D   CG
E   CD

10

A   RS
B   RU
C   RT
D   SU
E   ST

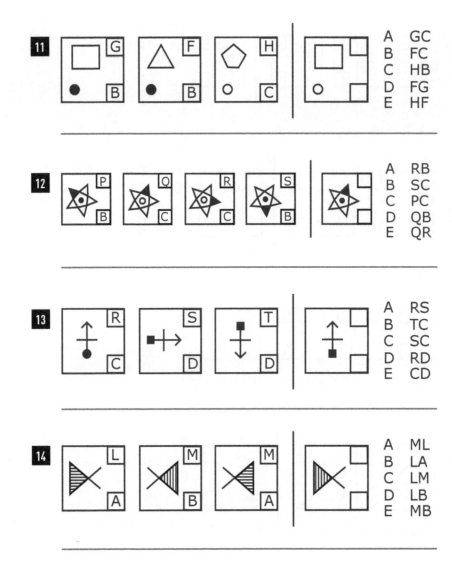

11

A GC
B FC
C HB
D FG
E HF

12

A RB
B SC
C PC
D QB
E QR

13

A RS
B TC
C SC
D RD
E CD

14

A ML
B LA
C LM
D LB
E MB

15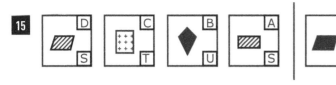

A   CU
B   DT
C   DU
D   BS
E   BT

16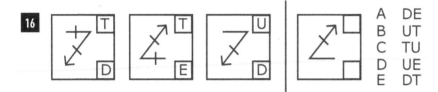

A   DE
B   UT
C   TU
D   UE
E   DT

17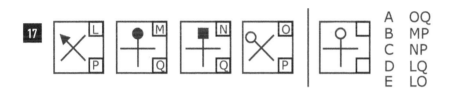

A   OQ
B   MP
C   NP
D   LQ
E   LO

18

A   TD
B   ST
C   SE
D   SD
E   TE

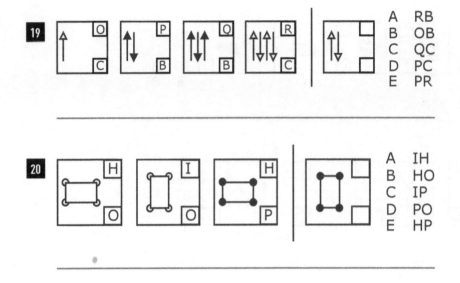

19

		A	RB
		B	OB
		C	QC
		D	PC
		E	PR

20

		A	IH
		B	HO
		C	IP
		D	PO
		E	HP

LESSON 4 PART 2: ANSWER SHEET

Mark your answer by putting a horizontal line in one of the boxes as in the example below.

Example:

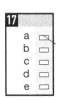

LESSON 5 Completing Grids

In this exercise, you'll be given a grid with one empty square while the rest of the squares contain shapes and/or patterns. You'll need to decide which of the possible five answer choices would best complete the grid.

Let's look at an example to remind you how to do this.

Example

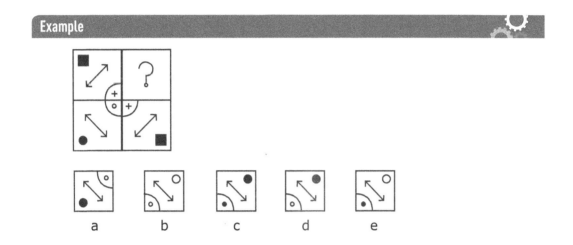

Here's how to solve this question:

➪ Note that there is a reflective pattern developing in the opposite corners of the grid. The answer will be a reflected version of the bottom left-hand square.

➪ Now turn to your answer choices and look for an arrow which lies diagonally, from top left to bottom right – they all have this so that doesn't help. Then look for an unshaded circle in the bottom left corner. Answers a, c and e don't feature this, so you can cross them out.

➪ Finally you need a solid shaded circle in the top right corner. Only choice d has all of these properties, so that is the one you should choose.

LESSON 5 PART 1

Now look at the questions below. Try to do each one as quickly as you can, but make sure you finish them all. When you've found the answer, mark it on the answer sheet on page 73. When you've finished, write down the time you took in the box above. Remember to get an adult to mark the test for you, then write down your score in the box at the top of this page.

You have five minutes to complete these, so work quickly.

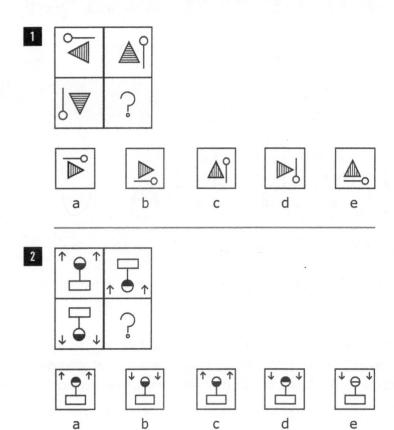

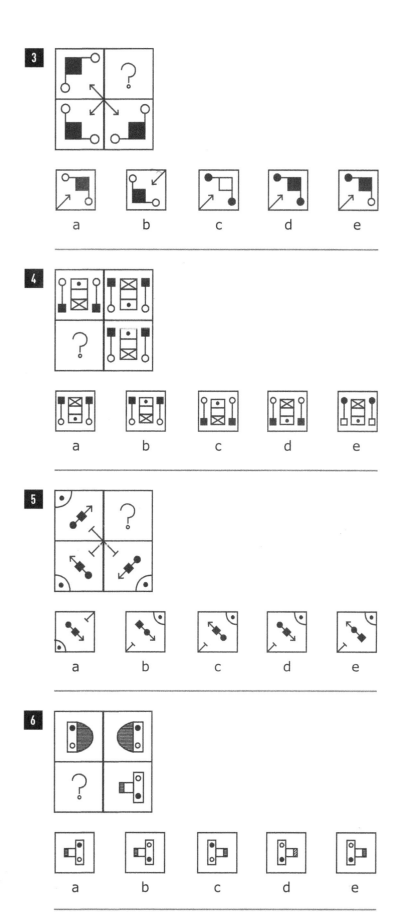

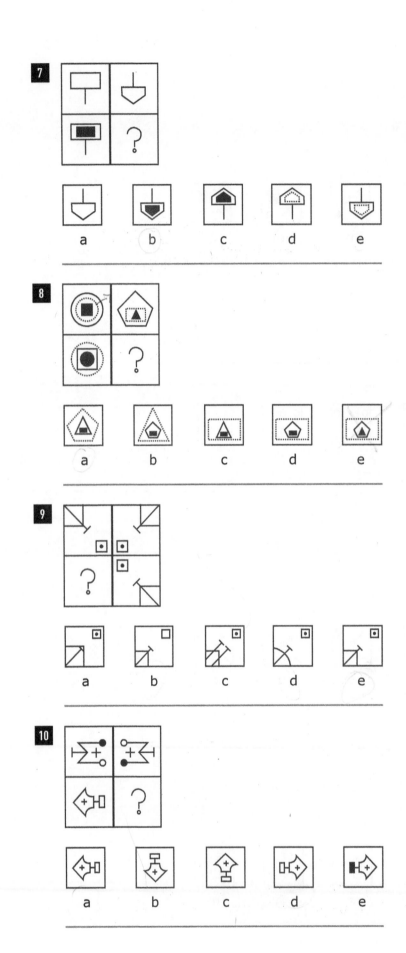

LESSON 5 PART 1: ANSWER SHEET

Mark your answer by putting a horizontal line in one of the boxes as in the example below.

Example:

   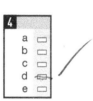 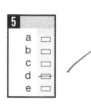

 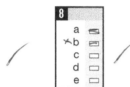 

How Did You Do?
Let's Find Out!

If you scored 8 or more out of 10

This is a good score – well done! Read the tips for speeding up then move on to the next set of questions.

If you scored fewer than 8 out of 10

You'll need to keep working hard to improve your score so check where you went wrong to help you learn from your mistakes. Read the tips for speeding up before you try the next set of questions.

TIPS FOR SPEEDING UP

- Remember you only have 30 seconds for each question, so you must work quickly on these but you should still be careful when you're marking your answer on the answer grid.

- If you're stuck on a question move on and come back to it at the end.

- Try to identify quickly whether you should be looking for a rotation, a reflection or sequence to be added to the missing part of your grid. Knowing what to look for will save you valuable time.

- Where a pattern is rotating, quickly sketch the answer on some scrap paper. Then see which of the possible answers matches your sketch – this will help you if a shape is tricky.

- For reflections and rotations you can pick up your paper and turn it to find what the shape would look like – then look for the answer that matches this!

LESSON 5 PART 2

My Time

My Score

The big practice

Here are the questions for your big practice. Try to do each one as quickly as you can, but make sure you finish them all. When you've found the answer, mark it on the corresponding answer sheet on page 83. When you've finished, write down the time you took in the box above. Again, get an adult to mark the test for you, then write your score in the box at the top of this page.

You have 10 minutes to complete these 20 questions. This is your final practice on this type of question, so do try your best.

1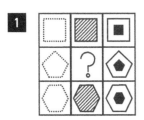

   a   b   c   d   e

2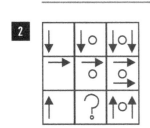

   a   b   c   d   e

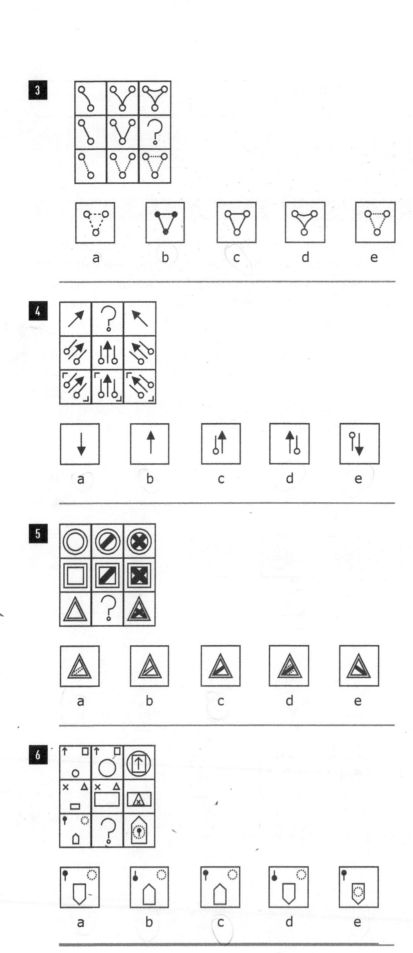

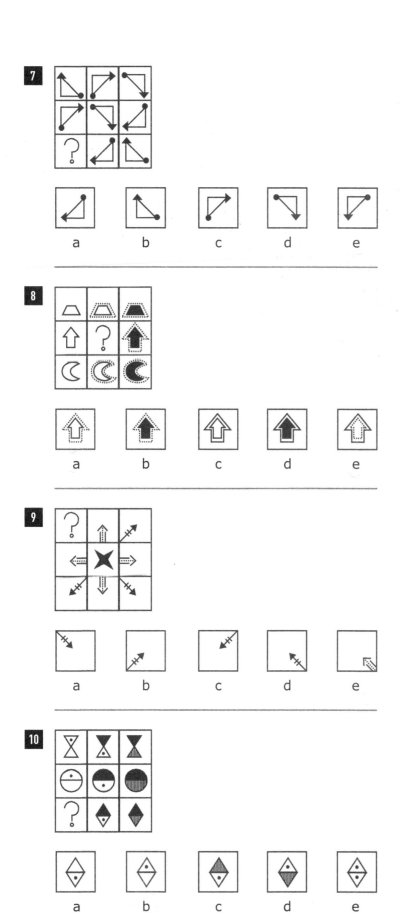

7

a b c d e

8

a b c d e

9

a b c d e

10

a b c d e

11

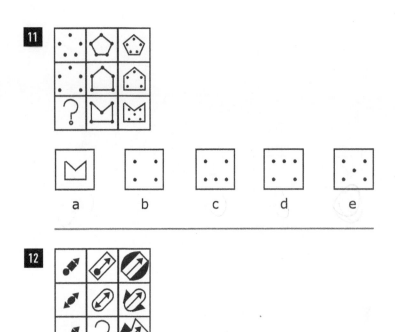

a	b	c	d	e

12

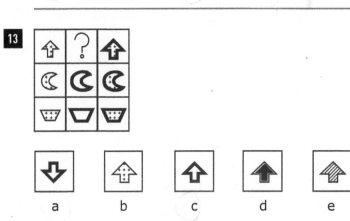

a	b	c	d	e

13

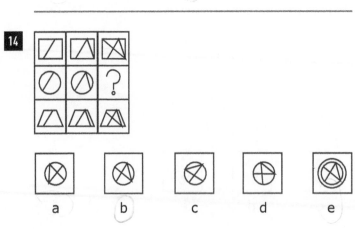

a	b	c	d	e

14

a	b	c	d	e

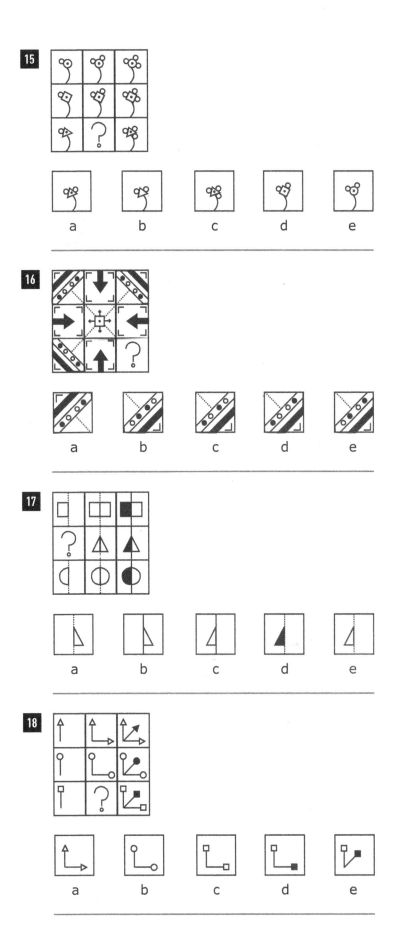

15

a   b   c   d   e

16

a   b   c   d   e

17

a   b   c   d   e

18

a   b   c   d   e

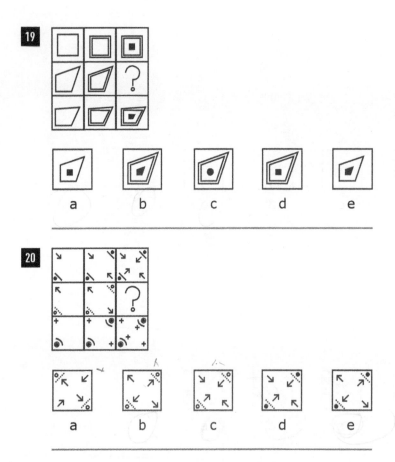

19

a   b   c   d   e

20

a   b   c   d   e

LESSON 5 PART 2: ANSWER SHEET

Mark your answer by putting a horizontal line in one of the boxes as in the example below.

Example:

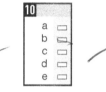

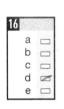

$$\frac{20}{20}$$

LESSON 6 Finding the Odd One Out

In this exercise, you're given five shapes or patterns. All of the shapes and patterns will have some property in common except one. You'll need to work out what property four of the shapes have in common to figure at which shape or pattern is the 'odd one out'.

As with other types of non-verbal reasoning, try looking at the different properties one at a time:

⇨ Count everything carefully

⇨ Check whether lines are solid or dotted

⇨ Check if the shading is the same

⇨ Check the sizes of the shapes

By going through each property methodically, eventually you'll find the odd one out. Let's look at an example to show you how this works.

Example

| a | b | c | d | e |

Here's how to solve this question:

⇨ You can see that the outer shapes are all basic shapes so you should look at the lines, to see if they all have solid lines. They do – so there is no odd one out there.

⇨ Next you should notice that some of the shapes have right angles. So you should check to see if they all do. More than one shape doesn't, so this won't help find the odd one out either.

⇨ Next look at the shape on the inside – notice how they are squares apart from b, which is a triangle. So <u>b</u> is your answer.

LESSON 6 PART 1

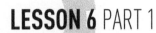

My Time

My Score

Now look at the questions below. Do each one as quickly as you can, but make sure you finish them all. When you've found the answer mark it on the corresponding answer sheet on page 89. When you've finished, write down the time you took in the box above. Remember to get an adult to mark the test for you, then write your score in the box at the top of this page.

You have five minutes to complete this task, but if you can do them more quickly, that would be great!

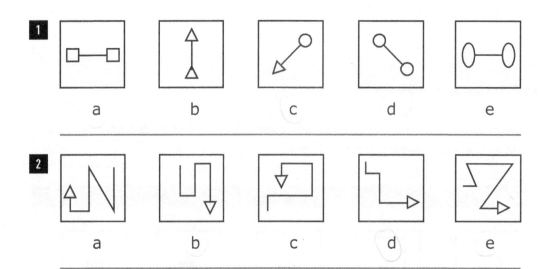

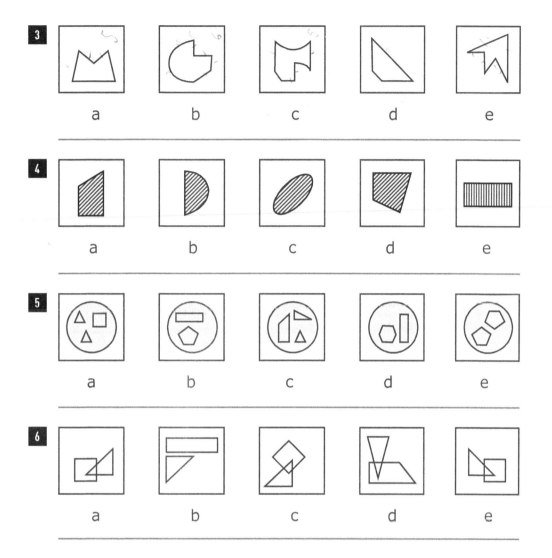

3

a b c d e

4

a b c d e

5

a b c d e

6

a b c d e

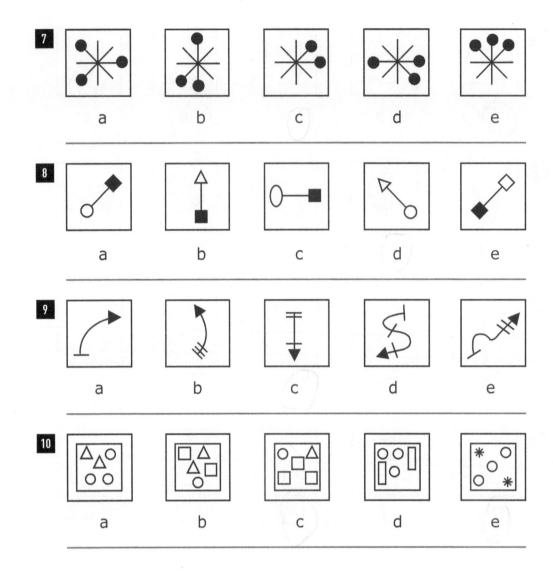

7

a b c d e

8

a b c d e

9

a b c d e

10

a b c d e

LESSON 6 PART 1: ANSWER SHEET

Mark your answer by putting a horizontal line in one of the boxes as in the example below.

Example:

 # How Did You Do?
Let's Find Out!

If you scored 9 or more out of 10

This score is a good one – well done. Read the further hints and tips for speeding up below then move on to the next set of questions.

If you scored fewer than 9 out of 10

Check where you went wrong, read the further hints and tips for speeding up below and then move on to the next set of questions.

Further hints

⇨ Remember you only have 30 seconds for each question so you must work quickly on these! Don't spend too long on a question that's tricky – you can always come back to it at the end!

⇨ Did you notice that in question 5 you had to count the sides of the shape inside the circles? Yes – they all add up to 10 sides apart from b, which is the odd one out. Look out for these!

TIP FOR SPEEDING UP

Try to go through the possibilities in an order. Think about which direction the shapes are facing, their shading, their size, their number. Move on quickly to the next property if one doesn't work.

LESSON 6 PART 2

My Time

My Score

The big practice

Here are the questions for your big practice. Try to do each one as quickly as you can but make sure you finish them all. When you've found the answer, mark it on the answer sheet on page 99. When you've finished, write down the time you took in the box above. Again, get an adult to mark these for you, then write your score in the box at the top of this page.

You have 10 minutes to complete these 20 questions, so work quickly. This is your final practice on this type of question, so try to do your best.

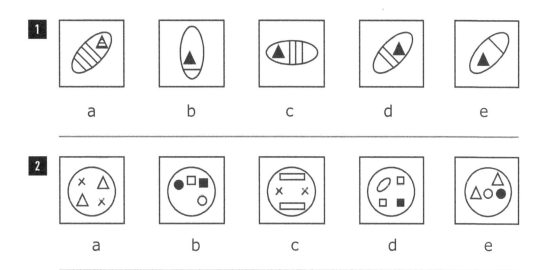

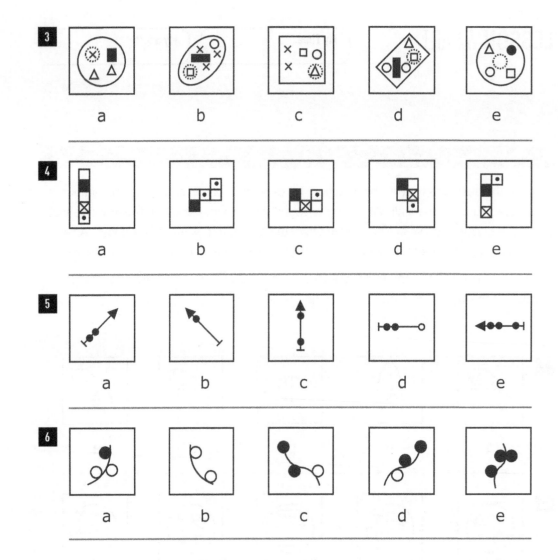

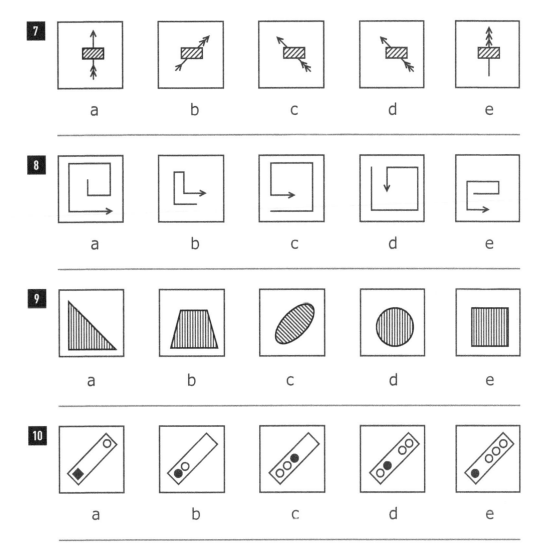

7

a   b   c   d   e

8

a   b   c   d   e

9

a   b   c   d   e

10

a   b   c   d   e

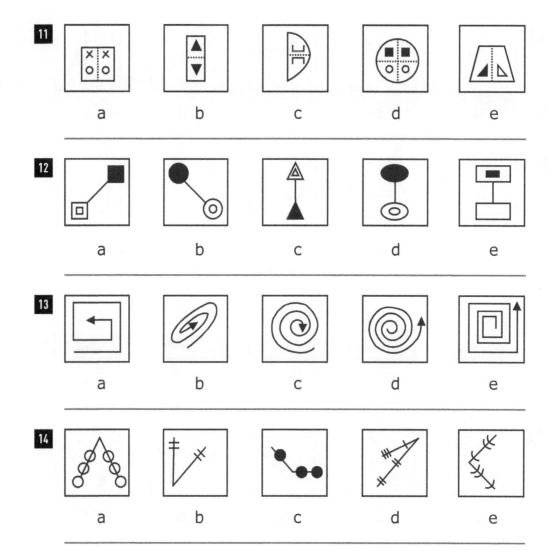

11

a   b   c   d   e

12

a   b   c   d   e

13

a   b   c   d   e

14

a   b   c   d   e

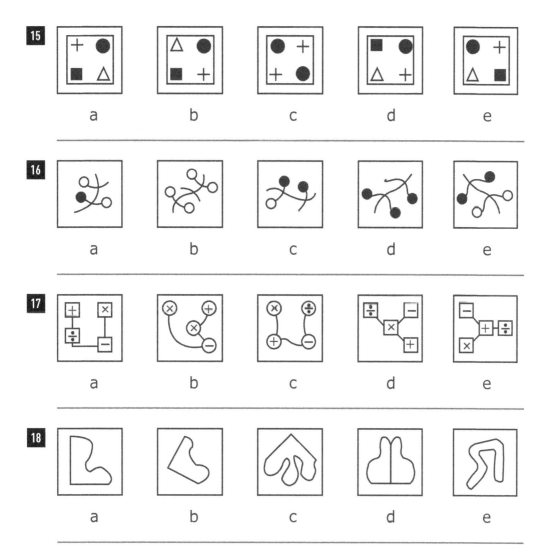

15

a b c d e

16

a b c d e

17

a b c d e

18

a b c d e

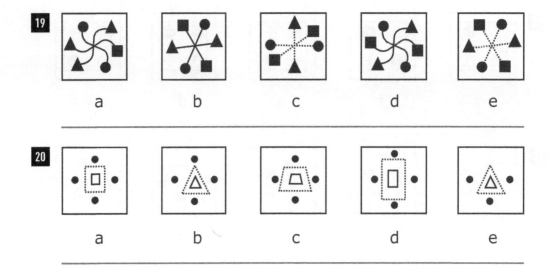

LESSON 6 PART 2: ANSWER SHEET

Mark your answer by putting a horizontal line in one of the boxes as in the example below.

Example:

SCORE SHEET

Use this sheet to track how well you've done. To find the average, add your scores and divide by 6.

LESSON	Part 1 score	Part 1 percent	Part 2 score	Part 2 percent
1				
2				
3				
4				
5				
6				

VOCABULARY BUILDER

Look at the words below and make sure you know what they mean. Look up any new words in a dictionary. If you've come across any other new words in the book, list those here too and learn their meaning.

Word	Meaning
Clockwise	
Right angle	
Dotted	
Solid	
Symmetry	
Rotation	

AND FINALLY...

Let me begin by saying 'well done'. You must have worked hard to complete this book, especially on top of your other homework from school!

Now that you've completed the second non-verbal reasoning book in the *Practise & Pass 11+* series, it's time to take stock. Have a look back at your scores and make a note of the kinds of question you found quite straightforward and scored well on and those that you found tougher and didn't score so well on. Taking a non-verbal reasoning paper is all about completing as many questions as you can in the time given, so keep practising the ones you found difficult.

Make sure you read back over the methods for each question – these will be helpful during your examination. When you're ready, it's time to move on to *Practise & Pass 11+ Level Three: Practice Tests* to complete a non-verbal reasoning paper under examination conditions.

And don't forget, if you need help with verbal reasoning, maths or English, there are books for each of those too to help you prepare for your exams.

⇨ *Practise & Pass 11+ Level One: Discover English*
⇨ *Practise & Pass 11+ Level One: Discover Maths*
⇨ *Practise & Pass 11+ Level One: Discover Verbal Reasoning*
⇨ *Practise & Pass 11+ Level Two: Develop English*
⇨ *Practise & Pass 11+ Level Two: Develop Maths*
⇨ *Practise & Pass 11+ Level Two: Develop Verbal Reasoning*
⇨ *Practise & Pass 11+ Level Three: Practice Test Papers*

Keep working and good luck!

ANSWERS

LESSON 1: part 1

1 d
2 e
3 b
4 e
5 a
6 c
7 b
8 e
9 e
10 a

LESSON 1: part 2

1 c
2 b
3 d
4 d
5 d
6 e
7 b
8 b
9 c
10 b
11 b
12 d
13 a
14 b
15 a
16 c
17 d

18 a
19 d
20 c

LESSON 2: part 1

1 b
2 e
3 c
4 b
5 e
6 d
7 d
8 c
9 c
10 e

LESSON 2: part 2

1 e
2 d
3 d
4 c
5 d
6 c
7 e
8 a
9 c
10 b
11 c
12 d
13 a
14 a

15 e
16 c
17 b
18 d
19 b
20 c

LESSON 3: part 1

1 d
2 c
3 b
4 a
5 d
6 a
7 e
8 d
9 c
10 e

LESSON 3: part 2

1 d
2 c
3 d
4 a
5 e
6 b
7 b
8 d
9 b
10 a
11 b

12 c
13 d
14 c
15 c
16 a
17 e
18 d
19 b
20 a

LESSON 4: part 1

1 e
2 c
3 a
4 b
5 c
6 c
7 c
8 e
9 d
10 c

LESSON 4: part 2

1 b
2 d
3 a
4 d
5 c
6 a
7 a
8 d
9 d
10 e
11 a
12 d
13 d
14 d

15 c
16 d
17 a
18 e
19 d
20 c

LESSON 5: part 1

1 b
2 d
3 a
4 d
5 d
6 e
7 b
8 a
9 e
10 d

LESSON 5: part 2

1 b
2 c
3 c
4 b
5 c
6 c
7 d
8 a
9 d
10 b
11 e
12 c
13 c
14 b
15 a
16 d
17 e

4 e
5 b
6 b
7 c
8 d
9 a
10 e

LESSON 6: part 2

1 a
2 d
3 e
4 b
5 d
6 b
7 e
8 b
9 c
10 a
11 e
12 e
13 c
14 c
15 c
16 b
17 b
18 e
19 a
20 b